CONTENTS

WELCOME TO SHOPVILLE!

Shopville is like no other place to shop. Really. Its rainbow coloured aisles are home to the cute and friendly Shopkins.

Come inside the Small Mart and meet Apple Blossom, Lippy Lips, Kooky Cookie, Strawberry Kiss, Cheeky Chocolate, D'Lish Donut, Chee Zee, and all of their friends.

They are all cheeky in their own way and will make shopping the best fun you could have. All you need is one empty shopping cart!

There are over 150 Shopkins to get to know and you'll quickly find some favourites – just make sure that they all get to hang out with their BFFs in the trolley!

Look out for extra cute, ultra-rare, special edition and limited edition characters; and once you've collected them all and got to know who's who, you can build your own Shopkins world! Start shopping now... Once you shop, you can't stop!

FRUIT & VEG

STRAWBERRY KISS

is a romantic at heart – she's a daydreamer with a huge imagination. She loves Valentine's Day and is usually busy thinking up her next poem, or drinking pink lemonade. She dreams about what's in the strawberry patch at the end of the rainbow.

APPLE BLOSSOM

is an adventurer with big dreams – ready to take a bite out of life. Her favourite colour is Granny Smith green and on a crisp autumn day, she'll be extra sweet, tart and a bit saucy because it's her favourite weather. Her signature dance move is The Worm!

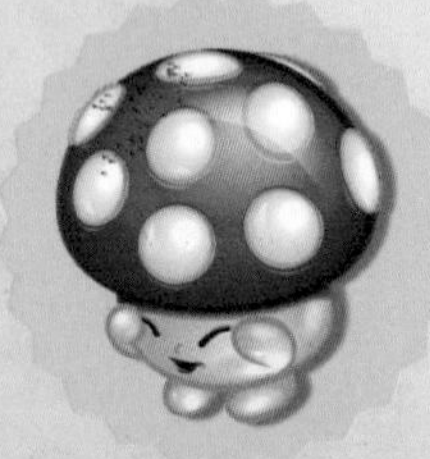

MISS MUSHY-MOO

is a complete softy but has a good head on her shoulders. She's not afraid to get mucky though as she loves making mud pies or dirt-bike racing! She likes dark, damp places and loved her vacation shopping for antiques on Portobello Road.

POSH PEAR

is always stylishly accessorised with her pink 'pear' of sunglasses! Friends say she's sweet, but a little spoiled. Her BFF is the fashionable Lippy Lips and she's often heard saying 'I can't help it if I have appeal'!

PINEAPPLE CRUSH

just can't get enough fun in the sun. She loves a tropical breeze and often daydreams about her best vacation ever, a luau in Hawaii. She's loved for her golden outlook on life and just loves a bit of sunbaking.

PANTRY

SALLY SHAKES

can't stop dancing and she adds flavour to life! She would Cha Cha down the aisles all day if she could, or dance to her favourite band, The Spiced Girls. Her best sports skill is the pinch-hit and she loves to go rock-climbing.

PEPPE PEPPER

might be sneezing all the time but he loves shaking it on the dance floor. He spices things up and is rarely seen without his BFF Sally Shakes. He likes to hang out with his cousins Jalapeno, Cayenne and Paprika, too. He just wishes he could stop sneezing!

SUGAR LUMP

is a real sweetie and she appreciates good manners. Her favourite hobby is perfecting the ultimate cup of tea and she says 'There's nothing sweeter than friendship.' Her favourite colours are brown and white, and she's a fanatic about organisation – storage cubes are her thing! Wonder why that is?!

BREAKY CRUNCH

likes to crank it up – he's an exercise junky! He loves working out, is full of energy and friends love him because he's ready to go at a moment's notice! He's definitely a morning Shopkin and his biggest fear is getting soggy! His BFF is Spilt Milk and he says 'Nothing can box me up!"

GRAN JAM

is the caring grandmother of all the Shopkins. She spreads love and slathers affection on everyone, sweetening their lives with her kind words! Most likely to be found knitting or doing the jelly roll dance move, she also loves filling in her scrapbook of memories.

TOMMY KETCHUP

just loves trolley rides – he wants to be in on all the action and is often heard calling out 'Wait, guys! Let me catch up!' Get that? Catch up, ketchup?! His BFF is Frank Furter and his nickname is Squirt! He loves to tell a saucy joke and his favourite colour is Tomato Red of course!

BAKERY

MINI MUFFIN

is exactly what she looks like – full of energy and sweet inside! She's an early riser and likes to go out for brunch. Her sports skill is yoga, especially at sunrise, and she'll often say 'Today is a bran new day'! Her BFF is Spilt Milk.

KOOKY COOKIE

is BFFs with Apple Blossom and Bread Head. She's shy and sensitive and loves to get stuck into a great book. She's also a whizz with acrobatics and loves somersaulting. Her sports skill is dunking and she is very good at thinking outside the cookie jar – and even has a secret talent for fortune-telling!

BREAD HEAD

is a chatterbox – there's no other way of putting it! He is always on the phone and is confident, independent and tells it how it is! He wears loafers and gets really tired of stale jokes. His greatest fear is getting sandwiched in a tight space!

D'LISH DONUT

often pops out of the oven singing 'Dough Re Mi'. Her friends say she's super sweet but also loves a bit of competition. She's always trying to perfect the perfect hole in one on the golf course and she loves basketball, too. She's a bit of an all-rounder and her favourite weather is a sprinkle of rain!

SWEET TREATS

LOLLI POPPINS

is just as sweet as sweet can be but can be a bit hard to get along with and is a bit stuck in her ways. She spends all her time making the other Shopkins laugh, and always has a smile but she dislikes lollygagging around and insists she's no sucker!

BUBBLES

is never happier than when singing a tune or trying a pop fly, as that's her sports skill. She's a real chatterbox and talks so much that she chews her friends' ears off. But they also say she's kind and caring and her BFF is Lolli Poppins.

LE QUORICE

is an acquired taste for many but she'll always stick by her friends. People say she's old fashioned but she insists she can still be the life of any party – it's the best place to show off those amazing Hopscotch skills! She wears colourful layers and is BFF with Mandy Candy.

CHEEKY CHOCOLATE

is a prankster who's never afraid to get dirty, and she's always laughing and having fun. Her favourite animal is the Chocolate Labrador and she is always breaking out in fits of giggles, melting hearts and pretending to melt herself!

DAIRY

SPILT MILK

is a morning Shopkin and is a bit of a klutz – he's always spilling things. He likes to stir things up and is a born risk-taker. His favourite hobby is just splashing about in the local pool and he loves skimming through comic books. He does cry over little things and likes the pouring rain!

CHEE ZEE

has a secret talent! He loves to rap with his BFFs Cheezey-B and Freezy Peazy and writes his own rap songs! He's a confident and passionate performer who loves to take centre stage and be in the limelight. He's afraid of mice and can be a bit crackers!

PARTY FOOD

SODA POPS

is super bubbly and just can't stop shaking it on the dance floor! She dislikes being shaken up and really has to cut her caffeine intake. Her friends say you can rely on her to add fizz to any party and she loves to refresh her wardrobe. She says, 'I hate to burst your bubble...'

WOBBLES

is a really cool Hip Hop dancer. No one can stop her once she starts jiggling! Her favourite song is 'Getting Jiggly With It' and she loves a good beat. She is a bit of a worrier who bounces from problem to problem, and her friends can see right through her!

WISHES

is a real party starter – her friends might say she's a bit of an attention-seeker too but she loves to throw surprise parties, sings 'When You Wish Upon a Star', and her prized possession is the candles from her first birthday. She says, 'You can have your cake and eat it, too!'

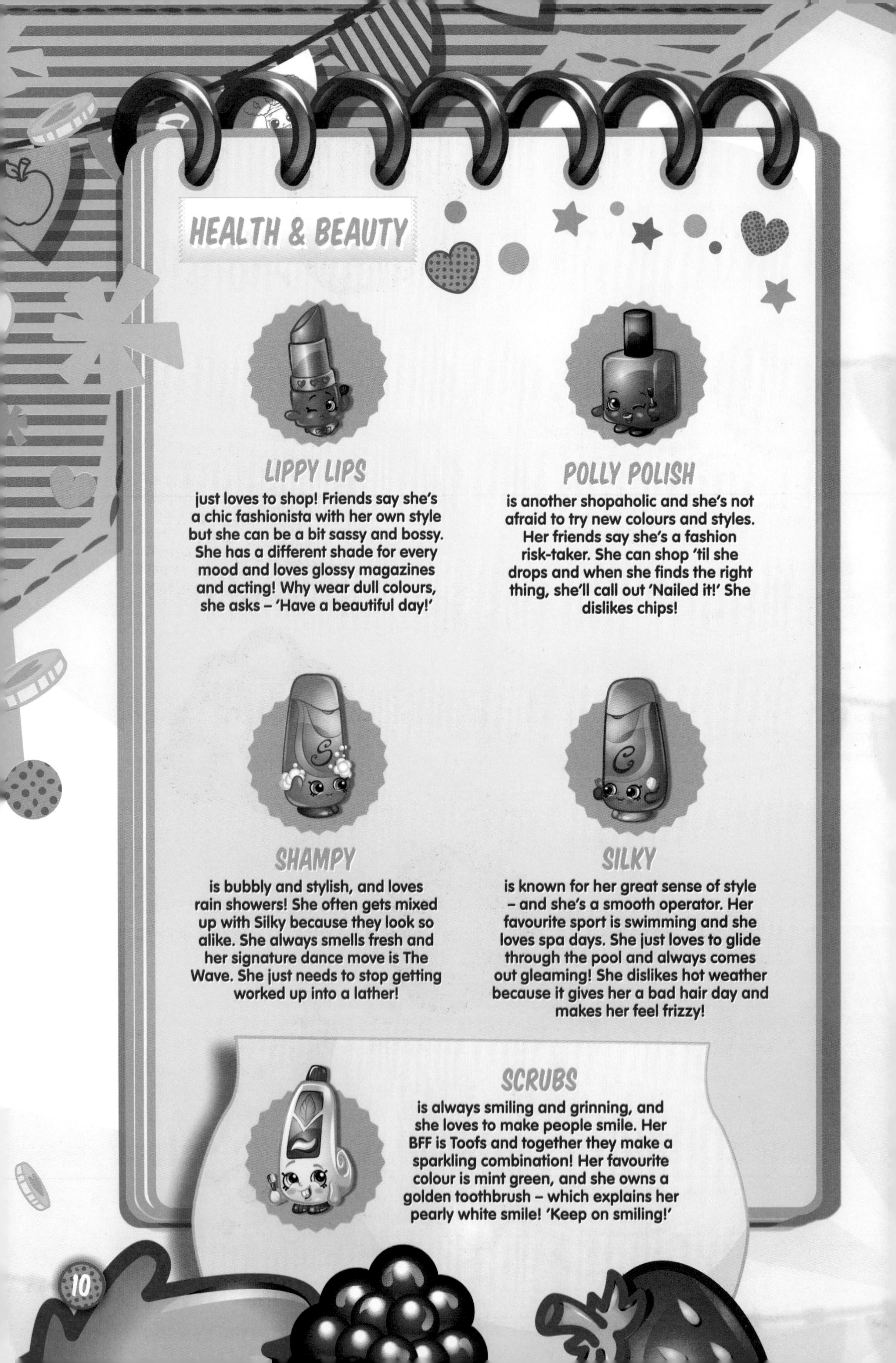

HEALTH & BEAUTY

LIPPY LIPS

just loves to shop! Friends say she's a chic fashionista with her own style but she can be a bit sassy and bossy. She has a different shade for every mood and loves glossy magazines and acting! Why wear dull colours, she asks – 'Have a beautiful day!'

POLLY POLISH

is another shopaholic and she's not afraid to try new colours and styles. Her friends say she's a fashion risk-taker. She can shop 'til she drops and when she finds the right thing, she'll call out 'Nailed it!' She dislikes chips!

SHAMPY

is bubbly and stylish, and loves rain showers! She often gets mixed up with Silky because they look so alike. She always smells fresh and her signature dance move is The Wave. She just needs to stop getting worked up into a lather!

SILKY

is known for her great sense of style – and she's a smooth operator. Her favourite sport is swimming and she loves spa days. She just loves to glide through the pool and always comes out gleaming! She dislikes hot weather because it gives her a bad hair day and makes her feel frizzy!

SCRUBS

is always smiling and grinning, and she loves to make people smile. Her BFF is Toofs and together they make a sparkling combination! Her favourite colour is mint green, and she owns a golden toothbrush – which explains her pearly white smile! 'Keep on smiling!'

FROZEN

FREEZY PEAZY

loves rapping with his BFFs Cheezey B and Chee Zee. Everyone in the Small Mall agrees he's super cool and the best rapper in the pod. He's always saying 'Be cool!' and his first memory is leaving the pod. He hates bad manners and is great with his Ps and Qs.

YO-CHI

brings a bit of cultural sophistication to the aisles. She's different every day and often has something exotic about her – you can see it when she swirls around the aisles. She's always trying a new topping and thinks every day should have a different flavour.

ICE CREAM DREAM

can cause her friends a bit of a headache sometimes LOL, but she's usually scoops of fun and her favourite hobby is Igloo Building. She hates it when she gets brain freeze and she can sometimes seem a bit drippy but her prized possession is a silver scoop!

POPSI COOL

loves to ice skate and her friends love to watch her. She also loves to chill out and rumour has it, she has a twin! They say she might be cold on the outside but on the inside she's warm and gooey. She's scared of getting freezer burn but says she can lick any problem!

WHICH SHOPKIN IS MOST LIKE YOU?

Every Shopkin loves to be someone's BFF, so which one do you think is most like you in every way possible? Answer the questions to lead you to your BFF Shopkin.

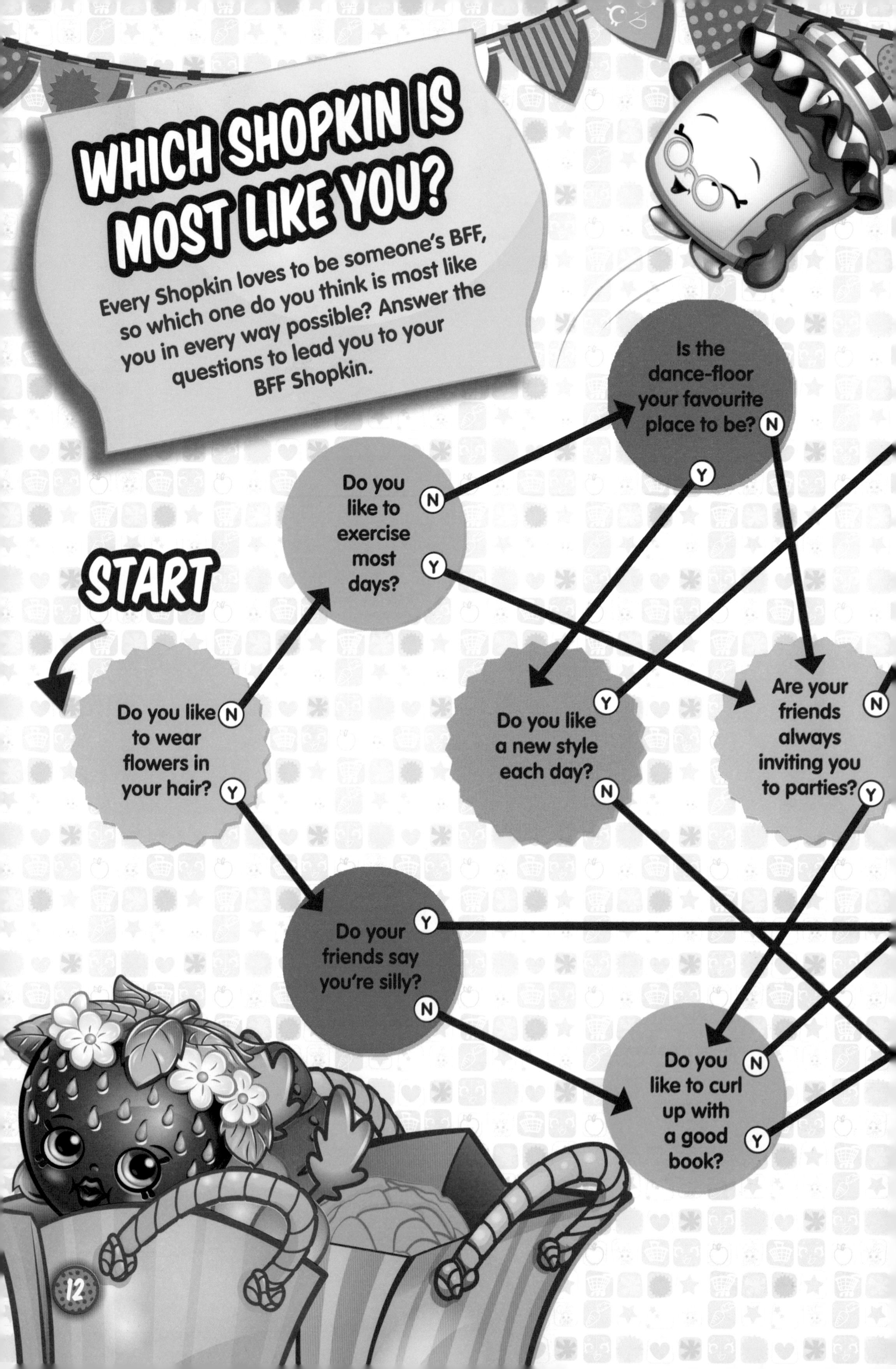

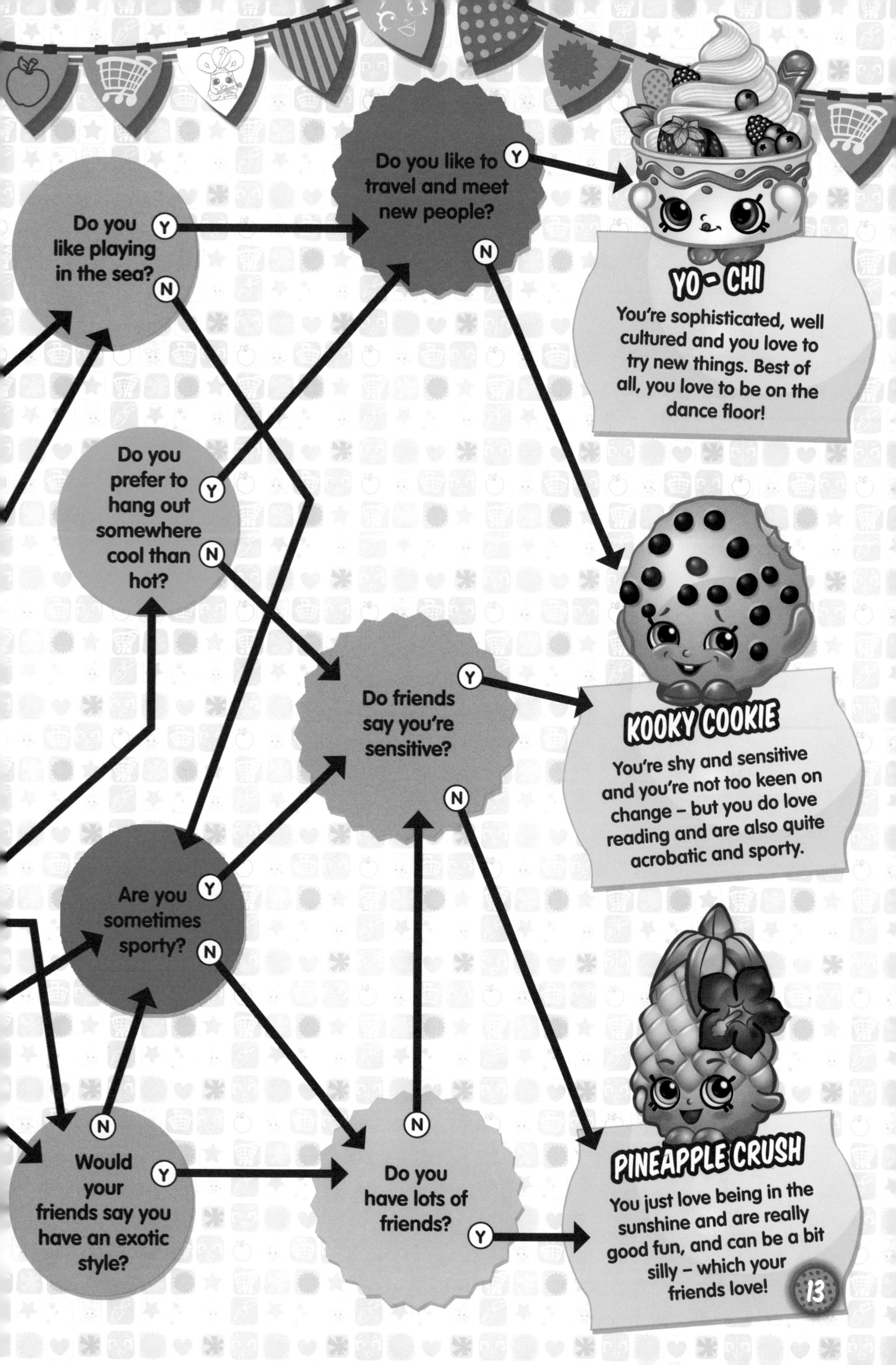

Do you like playing in the sea?
Do you like to travel and meet new people?
Do you prefer to hang out somewhere cool than hot?
Do friends say you're sensitive?
Are you sometimes sporty?
Would your friends say you have an exotic style?
Do you have lots of friends?
Y
N
YO-CHI
You're sophisticated, well cultured and you love to try new things. Best of all, you love to be on the dance floor!
KOOKY COOKIE
You're shy and sensitive and you're not too keen on change – but you do love reading and are also quite acrobatic and sporty.
PINEAPPLE CRUSH
You just love being in the sunshine and are really good fun, and can be a bit silly – which your friends love!

GROCERY MIX UP

The Shopkins are so friendly, they often pop to see their BFFs but now they're all mixed up and it's time for the mall to open. Circle the Shopkins in each section who need to move back to their own team! There are ten to find!

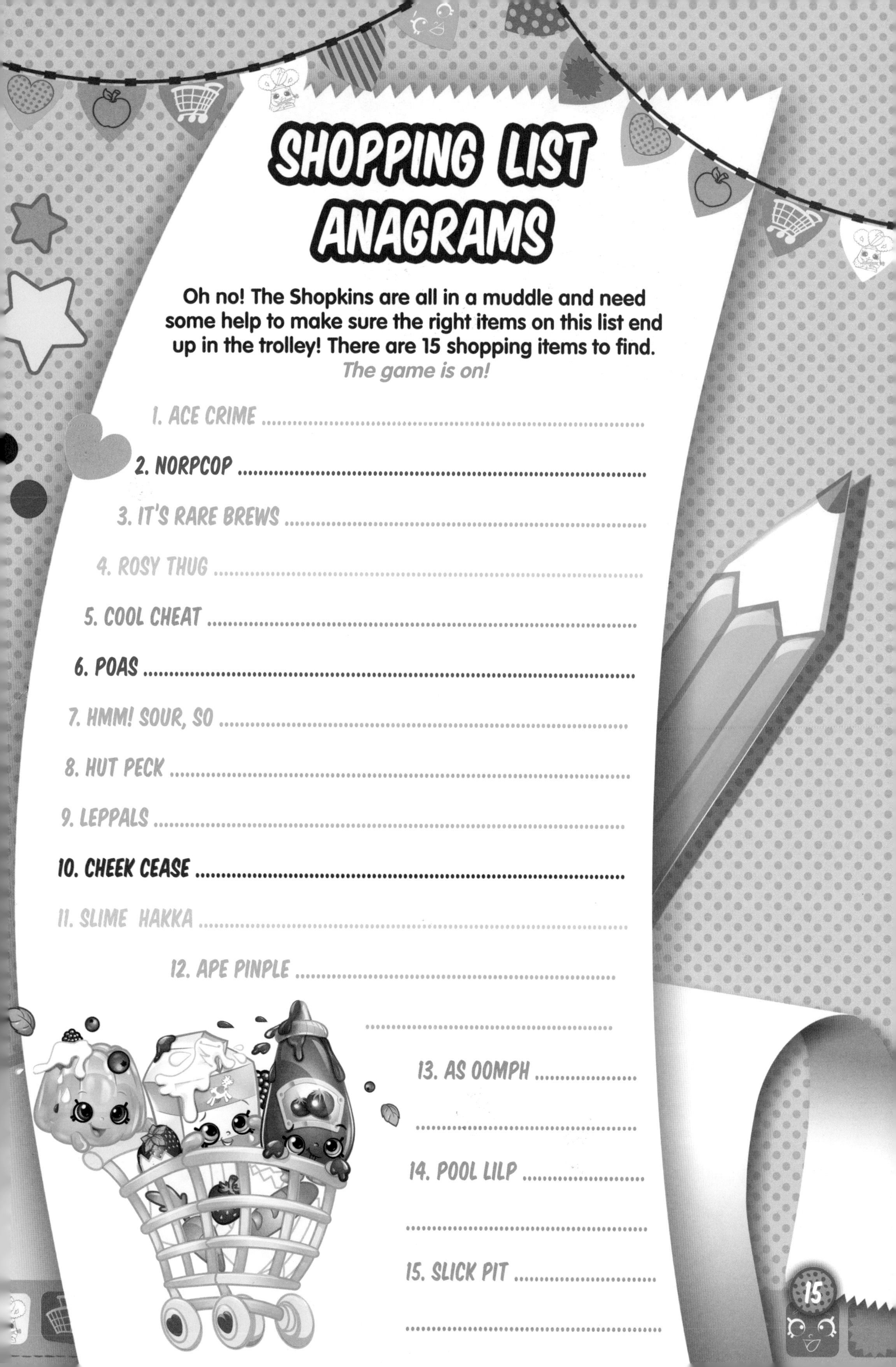

SHOPPING LIST ANAGRAMS

Oh no! The Shopkins are all in a muddle and need some help to make sure the right items on this list end up in the trolley! There are 15 shopping items to find.
The game is on!

1. ACE CRIME ....
2. NORPCOP ....
3. IT'S RARE BREWS ....
4. ROSY THUG ....
5. COOL CHEAT ....
6. POAS ....
7. HMM! SOUR, SO ....
8. HUT PECK ....
9. LEPPALS ....
10. CHEEK CEASE ....
11. SLIME HAKKA ....
12. APE PINPLE ....
13. AS OOMPH ....
14. POOL LILP ....
15. SLICK PIT ....

GET
COLOURING!

Bring these 8 Shopkins to life by colouring them in. Look through the activity annual to find the right colours or make up your own! Anything goes in the Shopkins world!

STORY: BREAKING NEWS

Shopville is in chaos this morning, after a major traffic accident. The aisles are blocked with rolling stock spilling out of trolleys. No one can get through to the checkout.

"Chaos indeed Apple Blossom! Some presumed maniac spilt over a defenceless shopping basket. It is still unknown who or what caused this tragedy but we'll be keeping our eyes open for this Shop-Villain!"

"We now go live to Strawberry Kiss who's about to report something amazing..."
WHAT ME? UM, A...AMAZING? I DIDN'T PREPARE ANYTHING!
Back in the studio Apple Blossom is stalling for time!
OUR AUDIENCE IS WAAAIITING, STRAWBERRY KISS!

AHH AHHH AHHH AHHH!
Oh no! Poor Strawberry Kiss is in panic! She doesn't know what to say and bursts into tears of Strawberry Jam!

EXCLUSIVE
AMAZING! STRAWBERRY KISS CAN CRY STRAWBERRY JAM TEARS! WHO KNEW?!

"And now live from the freezer it's Kooky Cookie with the weather!"
COLD...! BRR!!
BYE FOR NOW!

GUESS WHO?

Shhh! Shopkins love to play Hide and Seek. The clues will help you to guess their names, then write them below! Check you later!

1

I am a bit of a softy, but have a good head on my shoulders!

....

2

I always carry a handbag and try to look good! I am a bit spoilt though!

....

3

I am a fashion addict and love to give a bit of colour! I am a bit bossy too!

....

4

I love to be on stage. I am very confident and I am a little bit crackers!

....

5

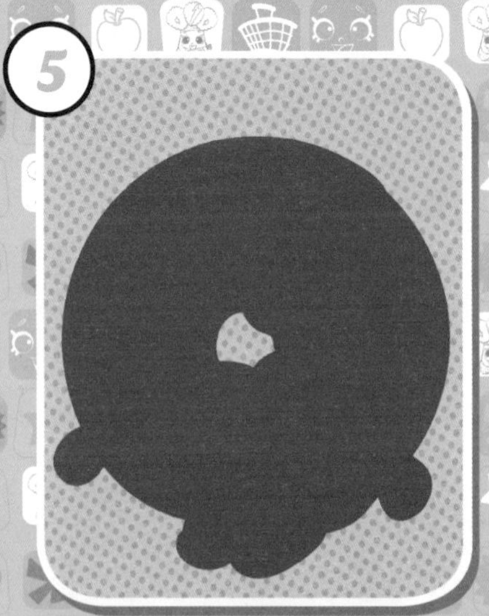

I am super sweet and love to play sports that have a hole involved, like golf or basketball!

....

6

I am as sweet as sweet can be and have a big smile! I love making other Shopkins laugh!

....

Shopkins™
Once you shop...You can't stop!
ONCE YOU SHOP, YOU CAN'T STOP!

COLLECTOR'S GUIDE

- COMMON $
- RARE $$
- ULTRA RARE $$$
- SPECIAL EDITION $$$$

FINISHES:

- GLITTER SHOPKINS™
- FROZEN SHOPKINS™
- METALLIC SHOPKINS™

There are lots of Shopkins to collect and they all want to be shopped by you! So here's a checklist for you to pull out and keep. Tick off each Shopkin as you collect. Keep your eyes peeled for ultra rare Shopkins!

FRUIT & VEG

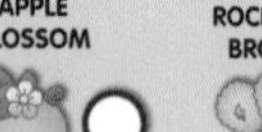

Name	No.	Name	No.
APPLE BLOSSOM	1-001	APPLE BLOSSOM	1-008
ROCKIN' BROC	1-002	ROCKIN' BROC	1-009
STRAWBERRY KISS	1-003	STRAWBERRY KISS	1-010
PINEAPPLE CRUSH	1-004	PINEAPPLE CRUSH	1-011
MELONIE PIPS	1-005	MELONIE PIPS	1-012
MISS MUSHY -MOO	1-006	MISS MUSHY -MOO	1-013
POSH PEAR	1-007	POSH PEAR	1-014

PANTRY

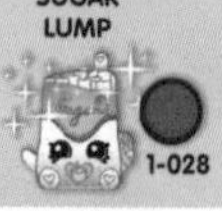

Name	No.	Name	No.
TOMMY KETCHUP	1-015	TOMMY KETCHUP	1-024
NUTTY BUTTER	1-016	NUTTY BUTTER	1-025
PEPPE PEPPER	1-017	PEPPE PEPPER	1-026
SALLY SHAKES	1-018	SALLY SHAKES	1-027
SUGAR LUMP	1-019	SUGAR LUMP	1-028
BREAKY CRUNCH	1-020	BREAKY CRUNCH	1-029
ALPHA SOUP	1-021	ALPHA SOUP	1-030
GRAN JAM	1-022	GRAN JAM	1-031
COOLIO	1-023	COOLIO	1-032

BAKERY

Name	No.	Name	No.
BREAD HEAD	1-033	BREAD HEAD	1-040
CREAMY BUN-BUN	1-034	CREAMY BUN-BUN	1-041
D'LISH DONUT	1-035	D'LISH DONUT	1-042
CHEESE KATE	1-036	CHEESE KATE	1-043
MINI MUFFIN	1-037	MINI MUFFIN	1-044
FLUTTER CAKE	1-038	FLUTTER CAKE	1-045
KOOKY COOKIE	1-039	KOOKY COOKIE	1-046

LIMITED EDITION

CUPCAKE QUEEN	1-137
BUTTERCUP	1-138
TIN' A' TUNA	1-139
TWINKY WINKS	1-140
PAPA TOMATO	1-141
SUNNY SCREEN	1-142

SWEET TREATS

      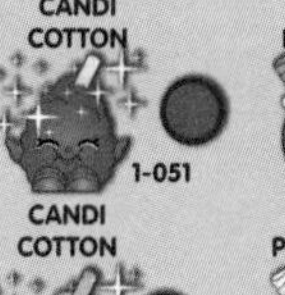    

- BUBBLES 1-047
- CANDY KISSES 1-048
- LE'QUORICE 1-049
- CHEEKY CHOCOLATE 1-050
- CANDI COTTON 1-051
- LOLLI POPPINS 1-052
- MANDY CANDY 1-053
- JELLY B 1-054
- MISS TWIST 1-056
- BUBBLES 1-057
- CANDY KISSES 1-058
- LE'QUORICE 1-058
- CHEEKY CHOCOLATE 1-059
- CANDI COTTON 1-060
- LOLLI POPPINS 1-061
- MANDY CANDY 1-062
- JELLY B 1-063
- MISS TWIST 1-064

DAIRY

         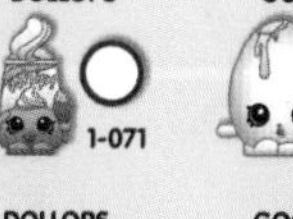 

- CHEE ZEE 1-065
- SWISS MISS 1-066
- SPILT MILK 1-067
- GHURTY 1-068
- MILLIE SHAKE 1-069
- FLAVA AVA 1-070
- DOLLOPS 1-071
- GOOGY 1-072
- CHEE ZEE 1-073
- SWISS MISS 1-074
- SPILT MILK 1-075
- GHURTY 1-076
- MILLIE SHAKE 1-077
- FLAVA AVA 1-078
- DOLLOPS 1-079
- GOOGY 1-80

      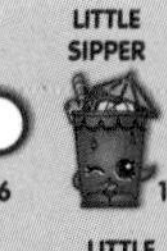       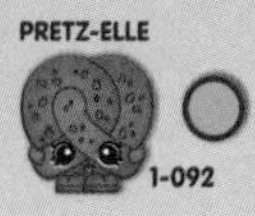        

- CRISPY CHIP 1-081
- PRETZ-ELLE 1-082
- WOBBLES 1-083
- RAINBOW BITE 1-084
- WISHES 1-085
- FRANK FURTER 1-086
- LITTLE SIPPER 1-087
- FAIRY CRUMBS 1-088
- CHEEZEY B 1-089
- SODA POPS 1-090
- CRISPY CHIP 1-91
- PRETZ-ELLE 1-092
- WOBBLES 1-093
- RAINBOW BITE 1-094
- WISHES 1-095
- FRANK FURTER 1-096
- LITTLE SIPPER 1-097
- FAIRY CRUMBS 1-098
- CHEEZY B 1-099
- SODA POPS 1-100

HEALTH & BEAUTY

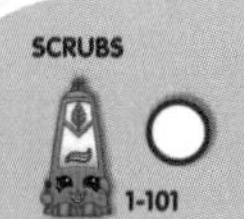 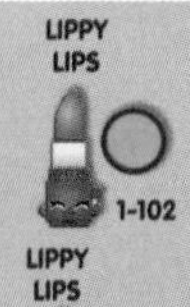      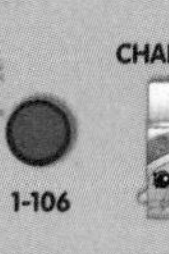 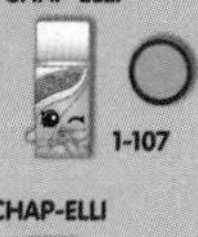 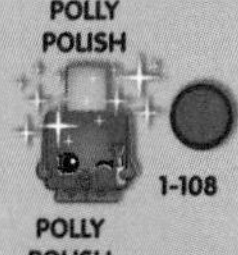 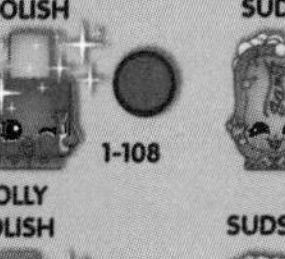 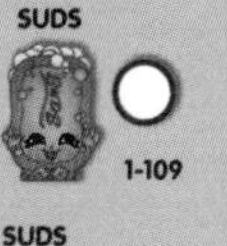  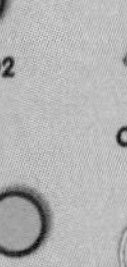  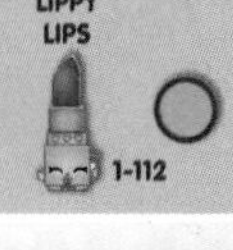       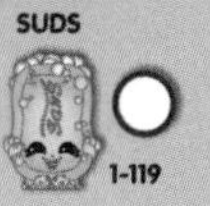 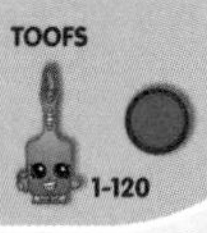

- SCRUBS 1-101
- LIPPY LIPS 1-102
- CURLY 1-103
- SHAMPY 1-104
- SILKY 1-105
- BUBBBLE TUBS 1-106
- CHAP-ELLI 1-107
- POLLY POLISH 1-108
- SUDS 1-109
- TOOFS 1-110
- SCRUBS 1-111
- LIPPY LIPS 1-112
- CURLY 1-113
- SHAMPY 1-114
- SILKY 1-115
- BUBBBLE TUBS 1-116
- CHAP-ELLI 1-117
- POLLY POLISH 1-118
- SUDS 1-119
- TOOFS 1-120

FROZEN

- ICE CREAM DREAM 1-121
- POPSI COOL 1-122
- YO-CHI 1-123
- COOL CUBE 1-124
- PA' PIZZA 1-125
- SNOW CRUSH 1-126
- FISHTIX 1-127
- FREEZY PEAZY 1-128
- ICE CREAM DREAM 1-129
- POPSI COOL 1-130
- YO-CHI 1-131
- COOL CUBE 1-132
- PA' PIZZA 1-133
- SNOW CRUSH 1-134
- FISHTIX 1-135
- FREEZY PEAZY 1-136

Shopkins™
Once you shop...You can't stop!
SO MANY
TO CHECKOUT!
NEXT

TANGLED BASKETS

Help each of these Shopkins find their way into the pink, green or blue basket. Follow the wiggly lines but don't get lost - you might not find them again!

....

....

....

TIME TO COOK!

It's time for you to make a delicious, gooey cheesy mushroom omelette with the Shopkins all keen to be involved! Draw the lines to the basket of the Shopkins ingredients you'll need to make it!

Googy

Peppe Pepper

Chee Zee

Alpha Soup

Sally Shakes

Dollops

Bread Head

Miss Mushy-Moo

Sugar Lump

Gran Jam

Lolli Poppins

Buttercup

Papa Tomato

Freezy Peazy

Nutty Butter

BASKET

Shop in style with the SHOPKINS
Lippy Lips and Posh Pear love to look good, and they can't have enough stylish accessories. A pink handbag is always best but they would love to be seen in the most glam, glitzy shopping bag.

ON THE SHELF

Today the shelves in the Small Mart are in chaos! The Shopkins have muddled themselves up and arranged themselves into patterns! Can you figure out which Shopkins completes each row?

PATTERN 1

PATTERN 2

PATTERN 3

PATTERN 4

WORD SEARCH

These cheeky little Shopkins are always hiding. Can you spot the 15 characters hiding in this word search? Circle the names when you find them.

SHHH!
THERE ARE TWO RARE SHOPKINS HIDING IN THERE TOO!

X Z W P O M S A L L Y S H A K E S
S L I Z N I V S E L B B U B P X V
J I I A C S R C Y U P K B J O C W
B P K B H S K H I R A E P H S O P
P P W F E M R E X K U R T E M D M
E Y Q S E U B E H A S R E L P Q E
P L E B Z S S K Y G Z G I L M L H
P I C M E H E Y M F T N K E U O E
E P I U Y Y Y C R P Z I O Z L O R
P S R R B M K H U K Z F O T R C Y
E Z O C D O T O E C F F C E A I X
P E U Y N O N C P F S U Y R G S X
P F Q R H N C O P Q T M K P U P B
E O E I O I U L A D P I O J S O R
R Z L A O U O A B W J N O Z B P M
B W P F J V F T G L I I K L K D M
Z M P Y Q Y B E C U P M N Q E D C

CLUES!

One of them is not afraid to get dirty hands and the other loves bopping around the aisles to the Spice Girls!

- C.......... C...............
- Lippy Lips
- Bubbles
- Le'Quorice
- S.......... S............
- Popsi Cool
- Sugar Lump
- Peppe Pepper
- Mini Muffin
- Kooky Cookie
- Pretz-elle
- Fairy Crumbs
- Miss Mushy Moo
- Cheezey B
- Posh Pear

BINGO TIME!

If you're let loose in the Small Mart, it's time to play! Are you ready to join in with the fun?

Get to know who's who and you'll soon have your own BFFs. So next time you're shopping, take this bingo card with you and start spotting!

Carefully cut out the bingo cards opposite and use some glue to stick them onto some card, or see if a grown-up can laminate it!

How to play:

1. Once you spot a Shopkin/item in the aisles, you can cross it out!

2. When you get a row of four items in a row, you call out Bingo!

If you're shopping with friends or with your family, then you can take another bingo card. There are two to cut out!

Remember to keep your eyes open so you don't miss a thing!

ROCKIN' BROC
BROCCOLI
GRAN JAM
JAM
SUNNY SCREEN
SUN SCREEN
SHAMPY
SHAMPOO
SPILT MILK
MILK
MILLIE SHAKE
MILK SHAKE
WOBBLES
JELLY
SODA POPS
FIZZY DRINK
FREEZY PEAZY
FROZEN PEAS
MINI MUFFIN
MUFFIN
MELONIE PIPS
WATERMELON
PEPPE PEPPER
PEPPER
CHEE ZEE
CHEESE
MISS MUSHY MOO
MUSHROOM
CHEEKY CHOCOLATE
CHOCOLATE BAR
TOOFS
TOOTHPASTE
POSH PEAR
PEAR
SILKY
CONDITIONER
PA' PIZZA
PIZZA
CRISPY CHIP
CRISPS
GO ON A SHOPPING SPREE!
SO MANY TO CHECKOUT!
YO-CHI
FROZEN YOGHURT
POSH PEAR
PEAR
SWISS MISS
SWISS CHEESE
GOOGY
EGGS
SCRUBS
SHOWER GEL
PINEAPPLE CRUSH
PINEAPPLE
SALLY SHAKES
SALT
BREAD HEAD
BREAD
LIPPY LIPS
LIPSTICK
D'LISH DONUT
DONUT
APPLE BLOSSOM
APPLES
BREAKY CRUNCH
CEREAL
STRAWBERRY KISS
STRAWBERRIES
GHURTY
YOGHURT
SHAMPY
SHAMPOO
CHEE ZEE
CHEESE
SUNNY SCREEN
SUN SCREEN
MANDY CANDY
SWEETS
TOMMY KETCHUP
TOMATO KETCHUP
PRETZ-ELLE
PRETZELS

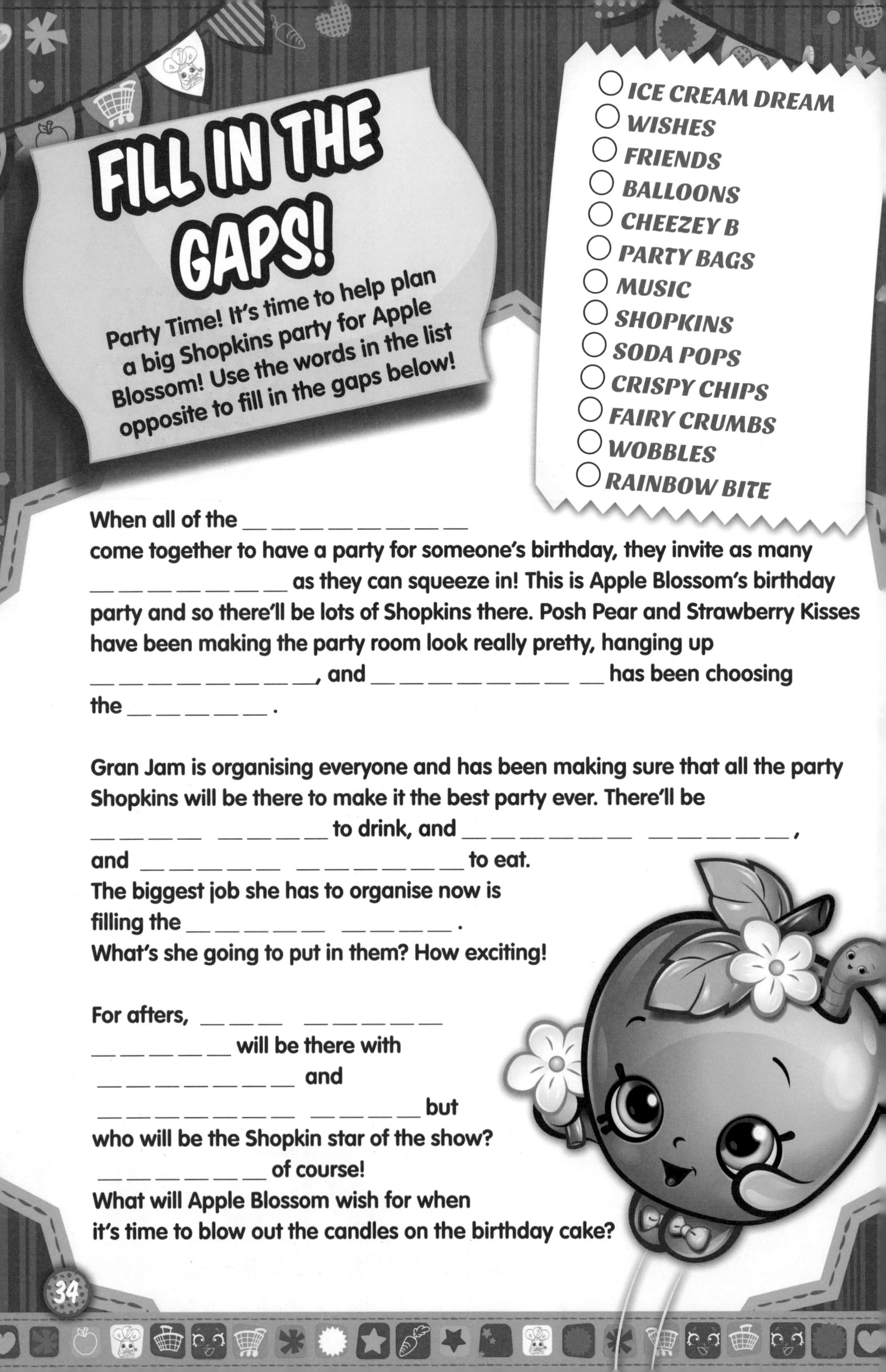

FILL IN THE GAPS!

Party Time! It's time to help plan a big Shopkins party for Apple Blossom! Use the words in the list opposite to fill in the gaps below!

- ICE CREAM DREAM
- WISHES
- FRIENDS
- BALLOONS
- CHEEZEY B
- PARTY BAGS
- MUSIC
- SHOPKINS
- SODA POPS
- CRISPY CHIPS
- FAIRY CRUMBS
- WOBBLES
- RAINBOW BITE

When all of the _ _ _ _ _ _ _ _
come together to have a party for someone's birthday, they invite as many _ _ _ _ _ _ _ as they can squeeze in! This is Apple Blossom's birthday party and so there'll be lots of Shopkins there. Posh Pear and Strawberry Kisses have been making the party room look really pretty, hanging up _ _ _ _ _ _ _ _, and _ _ _ _ _ _ _ _ has been choosing the _ _ _ _ _ .

Gran Jam is organising everyone and has been making sure that all the party Shopkins will be there to make it the best party ever. There'll be _ _ _ _ _ _ _ _ to drink, and _ _ _ _ _ _ _ _ _ _ _,
and _ _ _ _ _ _ _ _ _ _ _ to eat.
The biggest job she has to organise now is filling the _ _ _ _ _ _ _ _ _ .
What's she going to put in them? How exciting!

For afters, _ _ _ _ _ _ _ _
_ _ _ _ _ will be there with
_ _ _ _ _ _ _ and
_ _ _ _ _ _ _ _ _ _ _ but
who will be the Shopkin star of the show?
_ _ _ _ _ _ _ _ of course!
What will Apple Blossom wish for when it's time to blow out the candles on the birthday cake?

SHADOW SEARCH!

The shopping list below needs a letter beside each number. Match each shadow to its correct Shopkin.
To help you, draw wiggly lines between the Shopkins and their shadows! And... go!

Shopkins
Once you shop...You can't stop!
LIMITED EDITION
Hide & Seek
S
P
Shopkins
Once you shop...You can't stop!

Shopkins
Once you shop...You can't stop!
When you're mooching in store, you have to look around every corner and on every shelf because you don't want to miss the Limited Edition Shopkins!
To get you started, Gran Jam is looking for Papa Tomato, who's definitely in there somewhere, along with five other Limited Edition Shopkins.
Papa Tomato
Cupcake Queen
Buttercup
Sunny Screen
Tin' a' Tuna
Twinky Winks

NO-BAKE RAINBOW KOOKY COOKIES!

What could be better than getting Cheeky Chocolate, Kooky Cookie and lots of colour together in the same place? It sounds d'lish and very pretty! Too good to eat, maybe!

REMEMBER TO ASK AN ADULT TO HELP YOU!

You'll need a grown-up shopper to help with the mixing and melting but all you need is:

- 1 jar chocolate spread (200g)
- 600g cornflakes
- 180g melted dark chocolate
- 60ml canned coconut milk
- Some colourful sprinkles to decorate

How to make your own Colourful Kooky Cookies:

1 Ask a grown-up to help you melt some chocolate, and leave it to one side.

2 Spoon the whole jar of chocolate spread into a food processor. Pour the cornflakes and coconut milk in and mix until the cornflakes are covered in chocolate and all mashed up! 30 seconds will do the job!

3 Add the melted chocolate and mix again until it's completely mixed up.

4 Remove the gooey, sticky mixture and roll into round lumps with your clean hands! Decorate with sprinkles of your choice!

5 Leave to set in the fridge. They'll last for five days in there.

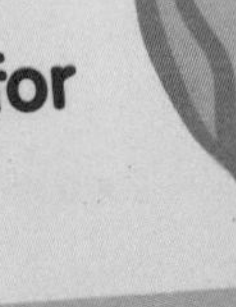

FRUIT SUSHI ROLL-UPS

SWING INTO THE STORE AND TELL THE SHOPKINS WHAT YOU'RE COOKING!

Yo-Chi would love these Asian inspired lunch-box treats because travelling and trying new things is a big yes-yes for this cultured Shopkin!

So for this you can mix together lots of Shopkins ingredients. Why not have a Shopkins swap party and make these with your friends? You can get some fruity ideas by looking at your Collector's Guide on page 24-25. Good thinking, hey!

All you need is:

- 3 tortilla rolls
- Chopped up fresh fruit of your choice, e.g. apples, mango, bananas, pineapple, strawberries, kiwi, pear. You'll need about three different fruits.
- 6 tablespoons cream cheese
- 3 tablespoons icing sugar
- 1 teaspoon vanilla extract

How to make them:

Mix the cream cheese, icing sugar and vanilla extract together with a hand-mixer until fluffy.

Spread the cream cheese over the tortilla rolls.

Line one side of the tortillas with chopped fruit, then roll it up so it's tight. Then enjoy!

WHO WILL YOU TAKE TO THE MALL?

Choosing the right friend to go shopping with is a big decision! You're going shopping with Apple Blossom and being so popular, Apple Blossom wants to take along a BFF too. So who will it be?

Follow Apple Blossom and the arrows on the trail and write down each letter along the way.

Write the letters in the spaces below to find out who she will take.

THE FRIEND THAT APPLE BLOSSOM WILL BE TAKING SHOPPING IS:

_ _ _ _ _ _ _ _ _ _ _ _

I SOMERSAULT MY WAY AROUND THE SHOP!
O
I LOVE TO TROLLEY RIDE!
R
I
C
I CAN'T MAKE A DECISION AND I AM A BIT OF A KLUTZ!
E
I LOVE TO SHOP BUT I AM QUITE BOSSY!
END

You might be in or out, so a door hanger to let people know is always handy!

Photocopy, or cut out and stick together this neat little door hanger and create a funky background for it. Give the Shopkins some colour, too!

FEELING DOTTY

Join the dots to find out which of the sweet little Shopkin fashionistas is hiding behind these glamorous sun shades! She says 'I can't help it if I have appeal'!

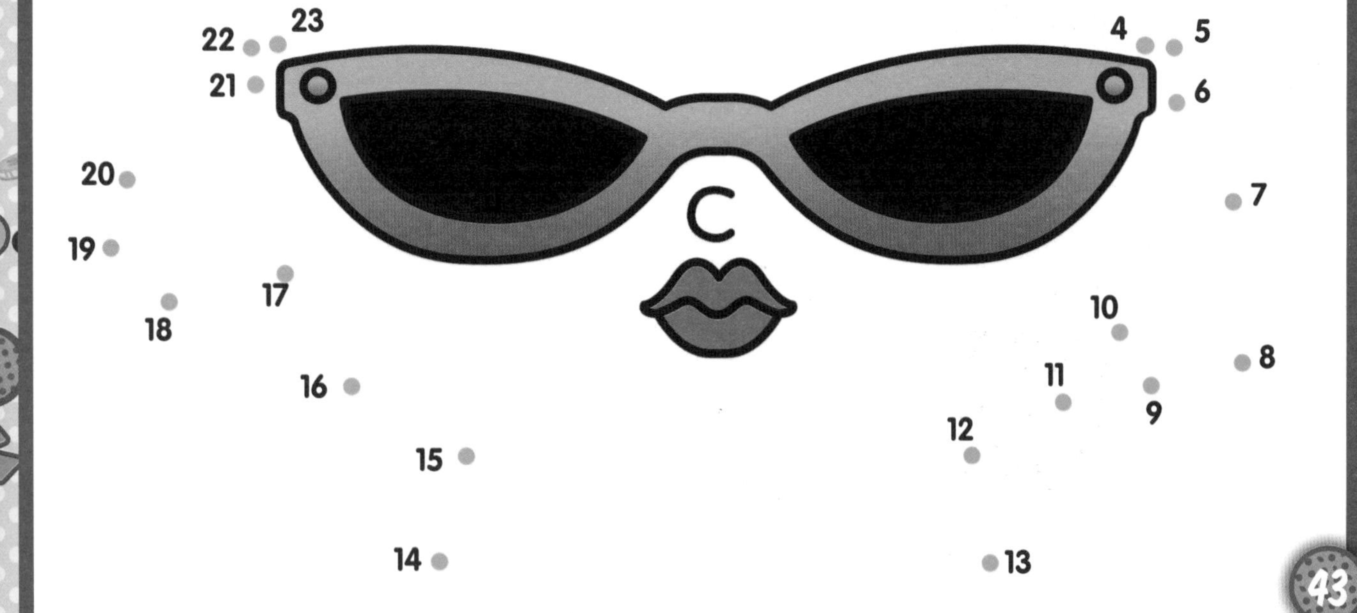

COLOUR BY NUMBERS!

Hey! These Shopkins really need colouring in don't they? To make them look good enough to be on the shelves in the Small Mart, just follow the numbers below.

3
7
3
7
3
12
11
11
7
11
2
5
3
5
7
2
4
7
1
7
2
12
7

SPOT THE DIFFERENCE

With so many Shopkins to get to know, you've really got to know your cookies from your fairy crumbs!

Can you spot the 6 differences between these two scenes at the Small Mart?

PICTURE 1

PICTURE 2

TURN OVER TO PAGE 48
TO CHECK YOUR ANSWERS!

CHECK YA LATER!

Well, all of the Shopkins have had a great time hanging out with you at the Small Mart. Did you have a great time with your friends in Shopville?

Did you find out anything new? If you want to see more of your Shopkin friends you can catch them live in the webisodes on the Shopkins website.

WWW.SHOPKINSWORLD.COM

Once you've said goodbye to your BFFs for now, you'll have to plan your next visit.

Start making your own Shopville at home and write your shopping list so that you can make a mad dash around the aisles and collect as many Shopkins as you can get your hands on!

ANSWERS

Page 14

Page 15

1. Ice cream
2. Popcorn
3. Strawberries
4. Yoghurts
5. Chocolate
6. Soap
7. Mushrooms
8. Ketchup
9. Apples
10. Cheesecake
11. Milkshake
12. Pineapple
13. Shampoo
14. Lollipop
15. Lipstick

Page 22

1 - Miss Mushy Moo
2 - Posh Pear
3 - Lippy Lips
4 - Chee Zee
5 - D'lish Donut
6 - Lolli Poppins

Page 27

Green basket - Spilt Milk
Blue basket - Le'Quorice
Pink basket - Tommy Ketchup

Page 28

Googy (Dairy)
Miss Mushy-Moo (Fruit & Veg)
Chee Zee (from Dairy)
Sally Shakes (Pantry)
Peppe Pepper (Pantry)
Buttercup (Limited Edition)

Page 30

Pattern 1 - 7, 2
Pattern 2 - 6
Pattern 3 - 4, 1
Pattern 4 - 5, 3

Page 31

Page 34

When all of the SHOPKINS come together to have a party for someone's birthday, they invite as many FRIENDS as they can squeeze in! This is Apple Blossom's birthday party and so there'll be lots of Shopkins there. Posh Pear and Strawberry Kisses have been making the party room look really pretty, hanging BALLOONS, and CHEEZEY B has been choosing the MUSIC.

Gran Jam is organising everyone and has been making sure that all the party Shopkins will be there to make it the best party ever. There'll be SODA POPS to drink, and, CRISPY CHIPS and FAIRY CRUMBS to eat.
The biggest job she has to organise now is filling the PARTY BAGS. Whats she going to put inside them? How exciting!

For afters, ICE CREAM DREAM will be there with WOBBLES and RAINBOW BITE but who will be the Shopkin star of the show? WISHES of course!
What will Apple Blossom wish for when she blows out the candles on her birthday cake?

Page 35

1 - B	5 - G
2 - F	6 - H
3 - D	7 - C
4 - E	8 - A

Page 36

Page 40

Le'Quorice

Page 46